Saxophone Exam Pack

ABRSM Grade 5

Selected from the syllabus from 2022

Name

Date of exam

C000001766

Contents

page

Saxophone consultant: Melanie Henry

The pieces listed above are just a selection of those on the syllabus that you can choose for your exam.

Whether you are taking an ABRSM Practical or Performance Grade, pieces are at the heart of your exam; after all, playing an instrument is all about exploring, performing, and learning through repertoire.

While this book contains nine pieces in a range of styles, the full syllabus has a wealth of other exciting repertoire that we encourage you to explore – to find pieces that really inspire you, that you connect with musically and will enjoy learning, and that will allow you to perform to your very best. You can pick a mixture of pieces from this book and the wider lists if you like – you just need to have one piece from each list, A, B and C.

If you are taking a **Performance Grade**, you also need to prepare a fourth piece which is entirely your own choice. Here you have even more freedom to choose music that really speaks to you, that you want to communicate to others, and that successfully completes your programme. It can be from the syllabus lists, or somewhere else entirely. Just be sure to check the 'Selecting Repertoire' section of the Performance Grades syllabus for important requirements and options for the own-choice piece (like standard and minimum length) and the programme of four pieces overall. Finally, you need to decide what order to play your pieces in and how you, the performer, will take your audience from the very first to the very last note, including moving from one piece to another, so that the performance forms a complete musical journey.

The separate syllabuses are available at **www.abrsm.org**. Whether taking a Practical or Performance Grade, enjoy exploring the possibilities on offer!

First published in 2021 by ABRSM (Publishing) Ltd,
a wholly owned subsidiary of ABRSM, 4 London Wall Place,
London EC2Y 5AU, United Kingdom
© 2021 by The Associated Board of the Royal Schools of Music
Distributed worldwide by Oxford University Press

Music origination by John Rogers, Julia Bovee and Katie Johnston
Cover by Kate Benjamin & Andy Potts, with thanks to Brighton College
Printed in England by Caligraving Ltd, Thetford, Norfolk, on materials
from sustainable sources.
P15387

A:1

Tarantella

No. 41 from *Vollständige Clarinett-Schule*, Part 1, Op. 63

Arranged by Alan Bullard

Carl Baermann
(1810–85)

Vollständige Clarinett-Schule Complete Method for Clarinet

© 2021 by The Associated Board of the Royal Schools of Music

A:2

Danse

from *La vie pour le Tsar*

Arranged by Vladimir Ivanov

M. I. Glinka
(1804–57)

La vie pour le Tsar A Life for the Tsar

Saxsequential

Paul Harris

B:1

Celtic V

No. 5 from *Celtic Collage*

Keri Degg
(born 1975)

mp *with a pure innocence*

AB 4045a

B:2

Andante

First movement from *Sonata for the Harp - with obbligato Flute*

Arranged by Althea Talbot-Howard

Joseph Bologne, Chevalier de Saint-Georges
(1745–99)

The cadenza figure included in this arrangement (bars 51–2) should be played in the exam.

© 2021 by The Associated Board of the Royal Schools of Music

B:3

All Because of You

Karen Street
(born 1959)

C:1

The Ragtime Dance

A Stop-Time Two Step

Arranged by David Blackwell

Scott Joplin
(1867/8–1917)

Not too fast ♩ = c.76

From bar 53 to the end, and following Joplin's original instruction, players may stamp the heel of one foot heavily upon the floor on the crotchet beats, to achieve the desired effect of Stop Time. This is optional in the exam.

Through the Trees

Cassie Kinoshi
(born 1993)

C:2

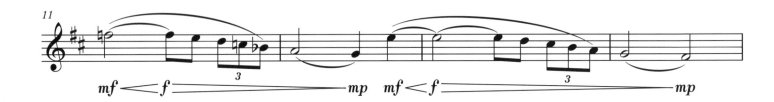

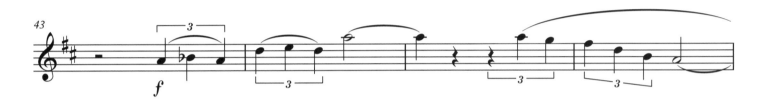

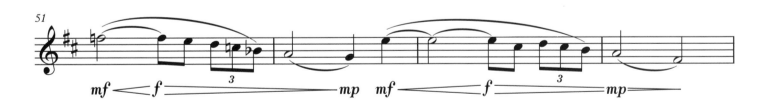

C:3

Festival Sax

No. 35 from *Sixty for Sax*

Alan Bullard
(born 1947)

Scales and arpeggios

SCALES

from memory
tongued *and* slurred

Scales and arpeggios

two octaves ♩ = 84

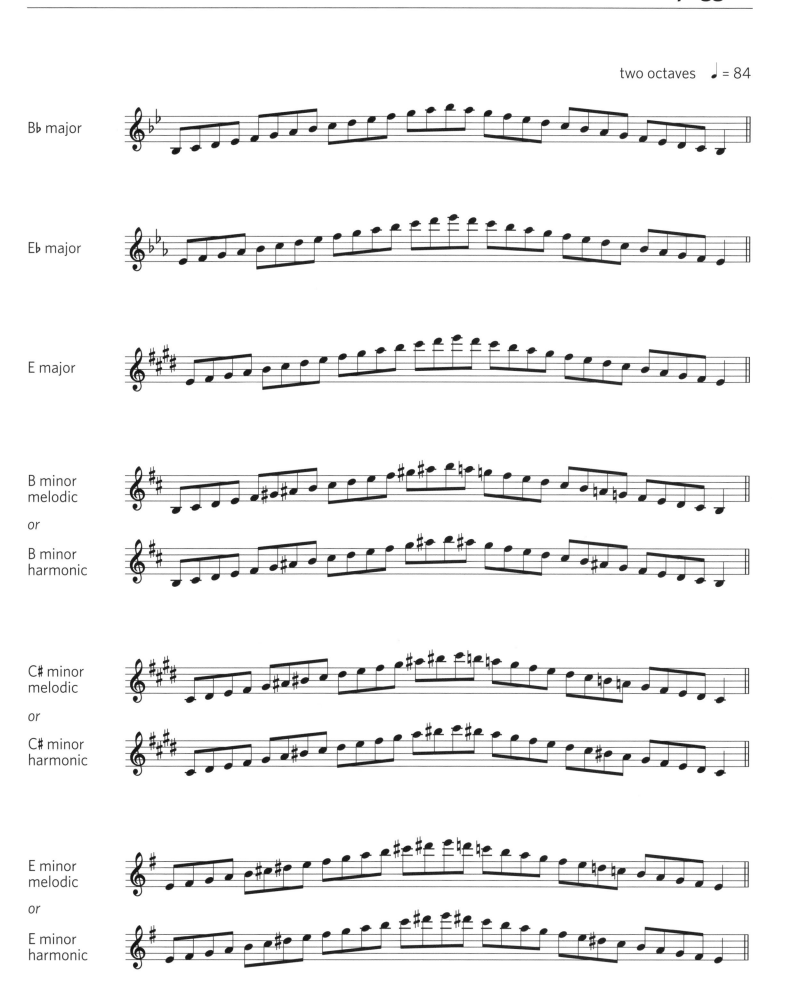

Bb major

Eb major

E major

B minor
melodic

or

B minor
harmonic

C# minor
melodic

or

C# minor
harmonic

E minor
melodic

or

E minor
harmonic

Scales and arpeggios

ARPEGGIOS

from memory
tongued *and* slurred

DOMINANT SEVENTHS

from memory
resolving on the tonic
tongued *and* slurred

DIMINISHED SEVENTH

from memory
tongued *and* slurred

CHROMATIC SCALES

from memory
tongued *and* slurred

Sight-reading

Sight-reading

Sight-reading

Sight-reading

19 Rock (Moderato)

20 Joyfully

21 Misterioso